# Susie and the Wise Hedgehog go to Court

Madge Bray

Published by Hawksmere Ltd
12–18 Grosvenor Gardens, London SW1

A CIP catalogue record for this book is available
from the British Library

ISBN 1 85418 020 7



Designed and typeset by Hawksmere Ltd
Printed in Great Britain by
MacLehose & Partners Ltd, Portsmouth

The wise hedgehog was taking a walk after lunch when he met Susie. She was sitting on the step beside the shed, squashing some crisps which were still inside the packet. She looked very worried. She was thinking and thinking.

'What's the matter, Susie?' said the wise hedgehog. 'You don't look very happy.'

'I'm not,' said Susie. 'My tummy's in a knot and I can't eat my crisps.'

'Oh dear,' the wise hedgehog murmured, soothingly.

'That police lady came again yesterday, you know, the nice one with the radio in her pocket, and she asked me more questions,' sighed Susie, 'and now she says I have to go to court.'

'Do you know what a court is?' asked the wise hedgehog.

'No, but I think it must be a horrid place because my mum looks very serious. Last night I could hear her and Auntie Rose talking downstairs for a long time after I went to bed. My friend Kerry Jane said it's a place where you play tennis. But I don't think it can be that. Is it? Oh, I don't know.

Do you know what a court is, wise hedgehog?'

The wise hedgehog smiled at Susie. 'Yes, as a matter of fact I do. Let me go and get the wise box and I can show you.' A few minutes later he returned with the wise box between his teeth and placed it on Susie's lap. 'Now,' he said, panting slightly from his exertions, 'press button one and look through the first window.'

'Ooh,' whispered Susie, 'that's a big building.'

'Yes, that's the court building. There are court buildings in most towns in the country. Courts are places where adults decide things.'

'What sort of things?'

'Well, there are different kinds of courts for deciding different sorts of things. Some courts decide about money when people argue about it. Some courts decide where children should live when their parents need help to decide between themselves. Other courts decide whether someone has done something they shouldn't have done, something that is against the law.'

'What are laws?'

'They are rules made to protect people. Rules that everyone has to follow, so that we can all get along with each other. When the police believe that someone may have done something which is against the law, they ask the court to hold a trial.'

'What is a trial?' Susie asked.

'The court holds a kind of meeting to listen to everybody's side of the story to decide if something is wrong.'

'So you have to go to court do you?' asked the wise hedgehog. 'It sounds to me as if you've been asked by the court to be a witness.'

'That's right,' said Susie. 'I think I remember now. That's what the police lady said. What is a witness? What does that mean?'

'Well,' said the wise hedgehog, scratching his nose, 'a witness has a very special job. The witness will know something important about what has happened. Do you know that many people live their whole lives and never get to be one?'

'Have you ever been one?' asked Susie.

'Yes, well as a matter of fact I have,' said the wise hedgehog, preening himself importantly. 'You know, it's a very special privilege to be able to help the court and one just has to be sensible and grown-up about it all. Do you think you could manage to do that?'

'I hope so,' said Susie, coughing nervously.

'I'm sure you can. You see, if the court thought you weren't old enough and sensible enough to help, you probably wouldn't have been asked.'

'Oh, I see,' smiled Susie, beginning to relax and feel important. 'What does a witness have to do, then?'

'Well,' said the wise hedgehog, 'what a witness has to do is to tell the court exactly what he or she knows about what happened. You can do that can't you?'

'Well, I think so,' said Susie.

'A witness must always, always tell the truth. Do you know what telling the truth means?' asked the wise hedgehog.

'I think so,' whispered Susie, 'but I'm not sure.'

'Well,' said the wise hedgehog, 'let's do some testing. Now supposing I said, "Susie is sitting on the step holding a bar of chocolate in her hand." Would I be telling the truth?'

'No, that's wrong because I've got a bag of crisps in my hand.'

'So would I be telling the truth?' asked the wise hedgehog again.

'No,' said Susie slowly, thinking carefully, 'you wouldn't, that's wrong.'

'Very good. Now let's try again. A bit more difficult, this time. Supposing I said, "Susie is standing up on the steps holding a bag of crisps."

‘Would that be the truth or would it be a lie? Take your time now and think carefully.’

‘Well, I have got some crisps in my hand,’ thought Susie, ‘but I’m not standing up, I’m sitting down.’ Eventually she said, ‘That would be a bit wrong, I think.’

‘I see,’ said the wise hedgehog, ‘so would it be the truth or a lie?’

'Well, I have got a bag of crisps in my hand,' said Susie, waving the

crisps in front of the wise hedgehog's nose, 'so that would be true; but I'm not standing up, so that part would be a fib.I think that would be a lie. Telling lies and talking fibs are the same thing, aren't they?'

'Yes,' said the wise hedgehog. 'I think you know the difference. The court will have to be sure of that too,' he added slowly. 'It's very important that you tell the whole truth. Now press the next button.'

'What's that little room for?' asked Susie. 'There's a lot of people sitting in there; what are they doing? They look as if they are just waiting.'

'That's the waiting room. Sometimes you have to wait quite a long time before it's your turn to go into the court room – maybe other witnesses may have to go in first. It's quite a good idea to take some crayons or a game with you so you won't be bored.'

'Will I have to go on my own?'

'Why of course not. You can go with a grown up whom you know and trust, someone to keep you company. They will probably be able to come into the court room with you. They will have to sit at the back and listen but they'll be there all the same.'

'Will it be a bit like when I had to sing by myself at the Christmas Carol Concert?'

'Yes, well, a little bit,' answered the wise hedgehog smiling. 'Press the next button; what can you see now?'

'Wow, I can see a big room with rows of seats and a big box thing and lots of people. And a high chair with a man in it. Who are all these people?'

'OK, OK, OK, just hang on a minute, let's take them one at a time,' said the wise hedgehog peering over Susie's shoulder. 'First of all do you see the man up on the high chair?'

'With the long, curly hair and the black robe thing?' asked Susie.

'Yes, he's called the judge.'

'What does a judge do?'

'Well, it's his job to make sure the trial is fair and that people do things in the court the right way according to the law,' explained the wise hedgehog. 'His long, curly hair is called a wig and it's part of his uniform. He will decide what is to happen at the end.'

'Is it always a man?' asked Susie.

'Usually; but sometimes it's a lady who's the judge.'

'Is it like being a boss?'

'Yes, I suppose it is,' said the wise hedgehog, thinking out loud, 'I suppose it is.'

'Sometimes there are two or three judges; they don't always wear wigs but they are still in charge. Now then, who do you think these people are sitting on these seats?'

'I don't know,' said Susie.

'Well, that's the jury.'

'Jury?' questioned Susie.

'Yes, that's a group of twelve people who are all over eighteen years of age. There are only juries when it is very complicated.

'Some courts don't have juries, some do.'

'Why are they there?' asked Susie.

'They have to listen very carefully to what everyone says and decide if someone did something wrong which is against the law.'

'There's a man sitting in front of the judge, what does he do?'

The wise hedgehog looked and said, 'He's called the clerk of the court, he does a lot of writing and helps the judge. Sometimes there's another person sitting with him who writes all the time on a machine.'

'Gosh,' said Susie wrinkling her nose, 'his hands must get very sore.'

'No, he's used to it,' said the wise hedgehog. 'It's very important that everything is written down so that no one forgets what was said.'

'Who are these people with short, white, curly hair and black gowns?' asked Susie.

'They have different names; sometimes they are called barristers or counsel or solicitors or lawyers – it depends which court you attend.

'What they do is ask the witnesses lots of questions. They are the people who do most of the talking in the court; they're very, very good at talking. They do it every day; they each ask questions in turn to make sure the judge and jury understand what's happened so that everyone understands what each witness knows. Sometimes they stand up and interrupt each other. Sometimes they make their voices sound very quiet and soft and other times they can make them very loud and sound as if they're very excited and shouting.

Sometimes they use long words.'

'Isn't it a bit rude to shout and interrupt each other?'

'We-e-e-ll' said the wise hedgehog, for he had to think quickly. 'It is when children do it . . . but when adults do it in a court room it's usually because getting to the truth is such a serious business that it must be got right. Sometimes different witnesses say different things you see.'

Susie stared at the picture in the wise box. Her eyes moved from one end of the picture to the other, concentrating very hard. 'Who is that person sitting in that place like a box?'

'That person is called the "defendant" or the "accused". He is the person who is on trial. Maybe he did something he shouldn't have done that is against the law. That is for the court to decide.Sometimes children who give evidence know the accused very well.

Now and again people we are close to do very silly things that are against the law, you know.'

Susie nodded slowly. She looked very serious. She was thinking carefully. 'Wise hedgehog,' she whispered, 'do some children worry because they think they may get someone into trouble with the court if they say what happened?'

'Yes they do, indeed they do,' sighed the wise hedgehog. 'But I think they must remember that if someone has done something wrong then he has got himself into trouble and that cannot be a child's fault, can it?'

'No,' said Susie slowly, 'I suppose not. What will I have to do when I go in?'

'When it is your turn, a person called an usher will come and find you and will take you to where you stand in the court room. That is a place called a witness box,' explained the wise hedgehog.

'A witness box – what's that?' asked Susie getting worried again.

'You could say that it's the truth-telling place where you tell only the truth; it's just a place in the court where you stand and say what happened. What you say is called evidence.'

'Oh dear,' said Susie. Her head had begun to buzz and her cheeks were getting quite hot. 'My mind is all of a muddle, I'll never be able to remember to say it properly. I know I shall do it all wrong.'

'Lots of people, even adults worry about that, but it's really not as bad as all that. All you have to do is tell the court what happened.'

'I bet it's worse than singing on my own at the Christmas Concert,' said Susie. 'I was really scared then.'

'I'm sure you were, but I'm sure you sang beautifully even though you were nervous, didn't you? I'm sure everyone clapped afterwards.'

'Yes, I did feel pleased after I came off the stage and mum said she was really proud because I had done my best.'

'That's right,' said the wise hedgehog in a very encouraging voice. 'That's all you can do when you're standing in the witness box. Do your best and remember to tell the truth.'

'What will happen when I stand in the witness box?'

'Usually the judge will talk to you himself. He will be very pleased that you have been able to come to the court to help by giving your evidence. Judges are very kind and listen carefully to what children have to say. Remember the judge was a little boy himself once and he will know that you might be worried.'

'What else do I have to remember in the witness box? I know I must tell the truth – but what else?'

'Usually the judge will begin by making sure that you know the difference between telling a lie and telling the truth.'

'So he might ask me tests like you did?' said Susie.

'Yes. Boys and girls will be asked to promise to tell the truth. If the judge thinks you can tell the truth you will be asked to promise to do that.'

'Are there any other things I have to remember?'

The wise hedgehog thought for a minute and said, 'You must remember always to be polite and if you don't understand what is being asked then just say "I don't understand", and then the question will be asked in another way.'

'What if I don't know the answer to a question?' sighed Susie.

'Just say, "I'm sorry I don't know." Try to remember to look at people when they talk to you and when you talk, look at the judge and jury and make sure they can hear you. The judge is the boss. Sometimes the people ask questions in quite loud voices and they seem very excited. It might seem as though they're getting cross with you but they're not, it's just that they have to be sure that you're really, really telling the truth.'

'But I'm not in trouble, am I?' asked Susie.

'No. It's very, very important that you remember that. You have come to the court because you have a very special job to do, that is to be a witness and help the court understand what has happened, isn't it?

'Yes, I think you understand about courts now. What do you think?' Susie nodded. 'Oh, there's one thing I forgot to mention,' said the wise hedgehog.

'Some courts understand that it is quite difficult for children to give evidence, especially if the defendant is someone they know.'

'Yes, it must be. That witness box is a bit big for children isn't it?' said Susie.

'That's right,' said the wise hedgehog. 'So do you know what some courts do?'

'No,' said Susie.

'Well, one of two things. Some courts put a screen between the child and the defendant so that the child can't see him or her.'

'Oh,' said Susie, 'that's a good idea.'

'Some courts allow the child

to go into another room away from the court room which has a camera and a TV screen in it. The child sits on a chair beside someone that they know and the barristers can ask the child questions even though they are standing in the court room. The child can see whoever is talking to them at the time on the TV screen and can hear through the TV set too. The child can't see the defendant at all then, but the court can see the child who is giving evidence on a television screen inside the court room itself.'

'Oooh,' said Susie. 'that's a clever idea.'

'Yes,' said the wise hedgehog. 'Adults do have some good ideas sometimes.'

'I think I'll eat my crisps now,' said Susie.

My tummy feels quite hungry. Thank you for helping me understand. I feel much better now. Would you like some crisps? I'm sorry they're so squashed, but I . . .'

'I understand perfectly,' said the wise hedgehog, before she could finish what she was saying, helping himself to a handful of crumbs.

'I thought you said it was rude to interrupt,' grinned Susie.

'Indeed I did, indeed I did,' said the wise hedgehog, chuckling.

Suddenly he was silent. He cocked his head to one side and looked intently at his toes.

'What's the matter?' said Susie.

'Oh . . . wait a moment,' said the wise hedgehog softly, still frowning a little. 'My wise mind has just had another thought pass through it.'

'What does it say? Oh, please tell me wise hedgehog, what does it say?' Susie bounced up and down on the step impatiently.

'It says . . . ' said the wise hedgehog carefully, '. . . it says I should give you a picture of myself to take with you, so that I can be with you in your pocket or in your hand when you give you evidence.'

'Well . . . what a very wise mind you have, wise hedgehog. I would really like a picture of you to take with me. I know it would help me not to worry about it all.'

'Well, in that case I shall manicure my prickles, and polish my nose and have my picture taken tomorrow.'

He patted Susie's hand reassuringly. 'It's a pleasure to see you back to your cheerful self again.' And he picked up the wise box and padded back under the hedge and curled up into a ball to go to sleep.

Here is a picture of the
Wise Hedgehog to cut out and keep